Core Knowledge Language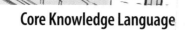

Snap Shots

Unit 1 Reader

obsolete

Skills Strand

GRADE 1

Amplify learning.

Core Knowledge®

Table of Contents
Snap Shots
Unit 1 Reader

Beth

I am Beth.

I am ten.

I am at camp.

Camp is fun.

Once Mom and Dad went on a trip to the camp. All of us were at the camp.

Dad and I went up on top of a path at the pond.

Mom got a snap shot of us.

This is the snap shot.

Then Mom let us snap some shots.

Dad got a snap shot of Mom.

I got a snap shot of a dog with a hot dog.

Nat

This is i̲s̲ Nat.

Nat is̲ a̲ kid I̲ met at camp.

I have lots of snap shots of Nat.

This is a snap shot of Nat with a fish.

13

This is is a snap shot of Nat on a raft.

Nat and I had lots of fun at camp. But then Nat's mom got a job in the U.K.

Nat left, and I felt sad.

The Trip to the U.K.

Nat went to the U.K., and I felt sad. But then Mom set up a trip to the U.K.

Mom and I went on a jet. Ships are fun, but jets are the best!

I got to sit next to the wing. I had lunch. Then I had a nap. Mom got this snap shot of the nap.

Nat met us at the end of the ramp.

I ran up to hug him.

Then Nat's mom, Dot, got us a cab.

This is a snap shot of us with the cab man.

Nat and I had a lot of fun. Then it was time for bed. Mom and I slept in a bed next to Nat's bed.

Bud the Cat

This is a snap shot of Nat's cat, Bud.

Nat got Bud from a vet. Bud had a bad leg. The vet had to fix Bud's leg.

Bud had to sit in a box with a cast on one leg.

Then Nat said, "Mom, can I have him? Can I? Can I? Can I?"

Dot said yes.

The Fish

This is a snap shot of Nat's fish.

The fish swim and splash and munch on fish snacks.

The cat can smell the fish. It can press on the glass. It can grab at the fish. But it can not get them.

The Flag Shop

Mom and I went in a lot of shops in the U.K. One of the shops was a flag shop.

The shop had the U.S. flag, the French flag, and the U.K. flag.

That's Mom in the snap shot, with the U.S. flag.

The U.K. flag has a big red cross on it. Nat and his mom held one up.

I got this snap shot of the two of them with the flag.

Which is the Best?

This is a snap shot Mom got. <u>All</u> <u>of</u> us had t<u>o</u> run up a bunch <u>of</u> steps t<u>o</u> get t<u>o</u> this spot.

Nat and I ran up fast. The moms had t<u>o</u> huff and puff t<u>o</u> get t<u>o</u> the top.

This next snap shot is <u>one</u> that I got. It is Nat with a bunch <u>of</u> big rocks.

Nat had Mom and Dot lift him up.

Then Nat s<u>ai</u>d, "Beth, get a snap shot <u>of</u> this! I am the rock on top! Get it?"

S<u>o</u> <u>whi</u>ch snap shot is the best?

The Bus Stop

Dot led us to a bus stop. At the bus stop there was a thrush.

Nat held up his hand. The thrush was all set to land on his hand, but then Dot said, "Nat, stop that!"

Nat let his hand drop.

At the bus stop, Nat said, "Beth, this is the best bus!"

I said, "Why? Is it fast?"

"No," Nat said, "it is not that fast."

"Then why is it the best?"

Just then, Nat said, "There it is!"

It was a big red bus with a top deck!

On the Bus

Nat and I sat up on the top deck of the big red bus.

The bus went past a big shop.

"That is <u>where</u> Mom shops," s<u>ai</u>d Nat. "That shop has <u>a</u>ll the best stuff!"

The bus went past a big clock.
A bell went ding, dong, ding,
dong.

"That is Big Ben!" said Nat.

"Who is Big Ben?" I said.

"Big Ben is not a man," Nat said.
"Big Ben is the bell that is in that
clock."

The bus went on.

"That is a posh spot there!" Nat said.

"Posh?" I said. "What is that?"

"A posh spot is where stuff costs a lot," said Nat. "Mom had lunch in there once, and it cost so much that dad got mad."

The Man in the Black Hat

All of us got off the bus. Nat led us up to a man in a black hat.

"Beth," Nat said, "that man will not grin."

"Why not?" I said.

"His job is to stand there as still as a rock and not grin," Nat said.

"I will do the best trick I can," Nat said. "But I will bet that man will not grin."

Nat did a trick and fell on his back.

Nat's trick got all of us to grin, but the man in the black hat did not grin.

"I bet I can get him to grin!" I
said.

I did a split, but the man did
not grin.

I sang a song and did a jig, but
still the man did not grin.

Mom got lots of snap shots of us and the man in the black hat. But there is not one snap shot where that man grins.

The Man in the Kilt

<u>Once</u> Nat and I met a man in a kilt.

I said, "<u>Why</u> is that man in a dress?"

Nat said, "That is not a dress. It is a kilt."

"A quilt?" I said.

"N<u>o</u>," Nat said. "A kilt."

"<u>Wha</u>t is a kilt?" I said.

Mom said, "The kilt tells us that the man is a Scot. The cloth on the kilt tells us <u>where</u> the man is fr<u>o</u>m."

"S<u>o</u> the kilt tells us his past?" I said.

"Yes," said Mom. "It is a bit of his past."

Mom got this snap shot of us with the man in the kilt!

The Map

<u>O</u>nce <u>a</u>ll of us w<u>ere</u> on a trip
<u>wh</u>en a dog ran up and bit the
map.

Dot said, "Bad dog! Stop that!
Drop that map! Drop it!"

But the dog did not drop the
map. The dog ran up the block
with the map.

Nat ran t<u>o</u> get the map, but Dot said, "It is just a map. Let the dog h<u>a</u>v<u>e</u> it."

Just then the dog let the map drop. Nat got it and held it up.

"H<u>ere</u> it is," Nat said. "But it's got a big rip in it."

"Well," Dot said, "I am just glad the dog bit the map and not <u>one</u> of us."

In the Cab

Dot got us a cab.

The cab man said, "<u>Where to</u>?"

Dot said, "The King's Pub."

"<u>What</u> is a pub?" I said.

"A pub is a spot <u>to</u> get lunch," said Nat.

71

"If it's the King's Pub," I said, "I bet it's posh. Will I get to sit with the king?"

"No," said Dot with a grin. "But this pub has got the best fish and chips!"

The cab man got us to the pub in a flash. Then all of us went in to have lunch.

73

Lunch at the King's Pub

At the King's Pub, all of us had fish and chips.

All of the pubs in the U.K. sell fish and chips. The fish and chips I had in the King's Pub were the best I had in the U.K.

Yum, yum!

Nat had a glass of milk with his fish and chips. Then his hand hit the glass.

Splash!

The milk went on Dot's fish and chips.

This snap shot tells it all.

The Punt

Dot said, "Let's rent a punt!"

"A punt?" I said. "<u>What</u>'s that?"

Dot led us to a dock. Th<u>ere</u> w<u>ere</u> t<u>wo</u> punts th<u>ere</u>, as well as a man with a long stick.

"Let's rent <u>one</u>!" I said.

All of us got in the punt. The man with the stick got in last.

The man said, "Kids, this punt can tip. If it tips, all of us will get wet. The best thing to do is to sit still and not stand up."

Nat and I sat still and did not get wet.

It was a lot of fun.

The Trip Back

The trip to the U.K. was so much fun. I was sad that it had to end.

When it did end, Nat and I had a hug. So did Mom and Dot.

Then Mom and I got back on the jet.

83

When Mom and I got back to the U.S., Dad met us.

"Dad!" I said, "I am glad you are here. I wish you were with us in the UK. Mom and I went on a punt and had fish and chips at a pub! Nat and I sat on top of a big red bus and went past Big Ben! It was the best trip!"

I got a map of the U.K. and hung it up.

I stuck red dots on all the spots Mom and I went to.

Mom got prints of the snap shots from the trip.

I sent the best ones to Nat!

CORE KNOWLEDGE LANGUAGE ARTS

SERIES EDITOR-IN-CHIEF
E. D. Hirsch, Jr.

PRESIDENT
Linda Bevilacqua

EDITORIAL STAFF
Carolyn Gosse, Senior Editor - Preschool
Khara Turnbull, Materials Development Manager
Michelle L. Warner, Senior Editor - Listening & Learning

Mick Anderson
Robin Blackshire
Maggie Buchanan
Paula Coyner
Sue Fulton
Sara Hunt
Erin Kist
Robin Luecke
Rosie McCormick
Cynthia Peng
Liz Pettit
Ellen Sadler
Deborah Samley
Diane Auger Smith
Sarah Zelinke

DESIGN AND GRAPHICS STAFF
Scott Ritchie, Creative Director

Kim Berrall
Michael Donegan
Liza Greene
Matt Leech
Bridget Moriarty
Lauren Pack

CONSULTING PROJECT MANAGEMENT SERVICES
ScribeConcepts.com

ADDITIONAL CONSULTING SERVICES
Ang Blanchette
Dorrit Green
Carolyn Pinkerton

ACKNOWLEDGMENTS

These materials are the result of the work, advice, and encouragement of numerous individuals over many years. Some of those singled out here already know the depth of our gratitude; others may be surprised to find themselves thanked publicly for help they gave quietly and generously for the sake of the enterprise alone. To helpers named and unnamed we are deeply grateful.

CONTRIBUTORS TO EARLIER VERSIONS OF THESE MATERIALS

Susan B. Albaugh, Kazuko Ashizawa, Nancy Braier, Kathryn M. Cummings, Michelle De Groot, Diana Espinal, Mary E. Forbes, Michael L. Ford, Ted Hirsch, Danielle Knecht, James K. Lee, Diane Henry Leipzig, Martha G. Mack, Liana Mahoney, Isabel McLean, Steve Morrison, Juliane K. Munson, Elizabeth B. Rasmussen, Laura Tortorelli, Rachael L. Shaw, Sivan B. Sherman, Miriam E. Vidaver, Catherine S. Whittington, Jeannette A. Williams

We would like to extend special recognition to Program Directors Matthew Davis and Souzanne Wright who were instrumental to the early development of this program.

SCHOOLS

We are truly grateful to the teachers, students, and administrators of the following schools for their willingness to field test these materials and for their invaluable advice: Capitol View Elementary, Challenge Foundation Academy (IN), Community Academy Public Charter School, Lake Lure Classical Academy, Lepanto Elementary School, New Holland Core Knowledge Academy, Paramount School of Excellence, Pioneer Challenge Foundation Academy, New York City PS 26R (The Carteret School), PS 30X (Wilton School), PS 50X (Clara Barton School), PS 96Q, PS 102X (Joseph O. Loretan), PS 104Q (The Bays Water), PS 214K (Michael Friedsam), PS 223Q (Lyndon B. Johnson School), PS 308K (Clara Cardwell), PS 333Q (Goldie Maple Academy), Sequoyah Elementary School, South Shore Charter Public School, Spartanburg Charter School, Steed Elementary School, Thomas Jefferson Classical Academy, Three Oaks Elementary, West Manor Elementary.

And a special thanks to the CKLA Pilot Coordinators Anita Henderson, Yasmin Lugo-Hernandez, and Susan Smith, whose suggestions and day-to-day support to teachers using these materials in their classrooms was critical.